CONTENTS

SECTION 1

Tests 1 to 12, covering:

Spelling: Spelling unstressed endings (e.g. **ant/ent**, **ery/ory/ar** (e.g. **able/ible**, to words ending **fer**); **i** before **e**; words that are

Word structure: Using prefixes to change the meaning of words; prefixes with hyphens; using suffixes to change word class; word families; building words from root words, prefixes and suffixes.

Vocabulary: Words with more than one meaning (e.g. different word classes, everyday meaning and subject-specific meanings); meaning of technical words (using word structure); synonyms and antonyms; formal synonyms for informal words.

Sentence structure: Sentences with main and subordinate clauses, including relative clauses; varying sentences for effect (type, length, structure); parts of sentences (noun phrase, preposition phrase, adverbial, parenthesis); modal verbs and adverbs to show possibility.

Punctuation: Using apostrophes and inverted commas accurately; commas, dashes and brackets for parenthesis; commas; colon to introduce a list; a single dash between clauses.

Grammar: Word classes; subject and object of a sentence; active and passive voice; linking adverbials for cohesion; changing words to achieve a more formal tone; figurative language.

SECTION 2

Spelling: Using known words to spell other words (e.g. **ent/ence**); exceptions to spelling rules (e.g. **ie/ei**, **able/ible**); revising spelling patterns; words with silent letters; strategies for tricky words that are often misspelt.

Word structure: More prefixes and suffixes; compound words (formal conjunctions); using root words to help with spelling; common roots and their meaning.

Vocabulary: Meaning of older vocabulary; figures of speech; choosing appropriate synonyms (to clarify meaning).

Sentence structure: Composing multi-clause sentences (to develop and link ideas); using the passive voice to change the focus of a sentence; reordering clauses for effect; conditional sentences; question tags.

Punctuation: Using a colon, dash and semi-colon between independent clauses; use of colons and semi-colons in lists; using commas to clarify meaning and avoid ambiguity.

Grammar: Use of perfect form of verbs; features of informal speech and writing; personification; cohesive devices.

SECTION 3

Spelling: Correcting spelling errors; using a dictionary to check spelling; double/single consonants; using word structure to spell words; homophones/words that are often confused.

Word structure: Words with related meanings.

Vocabulary: Word derivations; words with different meanings in different contexts; using a dictionary to check meanings; using a thesaurus.

Sentence structure: Editing sentences, making changes to enhance effect; forming a range of sentences to express ideas succinctly; use of ellipsis; using the passive for different effects.

Punctuation: Punctuating sentences to clarify meaning; using hyphens to avoid ambiguity; punctuating bullet points; punctuation for effect (ellipsis).

Grammar: Choosing vocabulary and grammar for formal writing; using the subjunctive.

A Warm-up

Write a sentence about computers.

1 In the past, _____

_____

2 Today, _____

_____

3 In the future, _____

_____

Underline the word that is **not** correct.

4 decide recent recide recite decent

5 sacrifice menace advice reverce reduce

Write the antonym.

6 inferior _____

7 backhand _____

8 minor _____

9 exterior _____

10 expansion _____

B Word work

1 Add the missing letters.

i e y

v a r __ __ t y   m __ s t __ r y

2 Write the plural forms of both words.

_____   _____

3 Add the suffix **er** or **or**.

perform ____   invent ____   collect ____

4 Describe the words you have created.

_____

_____

Write three more words of this type.

5 ending **er** _____

6 ending **or** _____

Write different definitions of each word.

7 **hamper** (verb) _____

8 **hamper** (noun) _____

9 **coast** (verb) _____

10 **coast** (noun) _____

C Sentence work

Add a preposition phrase to the start of the sentence.

1 _____ it was completely dark.

2 _____ it was completely dark.

3 _____ the man turned and spoke.

4 _____ the man turned and spoke.

Write more formal verbs that could replace the underlined words.

5 The RSPCA asked people to help as it tried to cope with the crisis. _____

6 Residents left the meeting, saying that the situation had not been sorted.

_____

7 If you want further information, go to the website where you can find out more.

Add punctuation and capital letters to these examples of direct speech.

8   Indira said It is very sad. We all feel let down

9   It's not fair Mick complained I want to go with you

10   It was bitterly cold explained Bill and the streets were covered with ice

X There is only one correct answer.   X There is more than one correct answer.

A   Warm-up

Continue the sentence after the subordinating conjunction.

1   He stayed with Jen until _____

2   He stayed with Jen as long as _____

_____

Write four words formed by adding a prefix or suffix to the word **port**.

3   _____   5   _____

4   _____   6   _____

7   Add the same suffix to both words to make them into adjectives.

excuse _____   charge _____

8   Add a different prefix to each of the words you have made. Write the new words.

_____

Write a synonym for the word in **bold**.

9   **persuade** _____

10   **discuss** _____

B   Word work

Underline the word that is spelt correctly.

1   dependent   observent

2   innocant   tolerant

3   convenient   ignorent

4   expectant   obediant

5   Write the correct spellings of the words that were wrongly spelt.

_____

6   Add the correct spelling of the ending that sounds like 'shun'.

techni_____   comple_____

profe_____   conclu_____

7   What kind of words have you made by adding the suffixes? Underline the correct answer.

verbs   nouns   adjectives

Write two more formal synonyms of the words in **bold**.

8   I'm **whacked**.   _____

9   It's a **phoney**.   _____

10   We must **come clean**.   _____

C   Sentence work

Combine the two sentences by using a relative clause.

1   A theatre is a public building. Plays are performed there.

_____

2   An orchestra is a group of musicians. They play many kinds of instruments.

_____

3   A thermostat is a device on a heater. It controls the temperature.

_____

Underline the adverb and explain why the writer has used it.

4   Perhaps she could have helped me. _____

5   He is very clever. _____

6   Unfortunately, City won 2–0. _____

Complete the phrase by writing in an item or items belonging to the characters. Use the correct punctuation.

7   the pirates _____   9   the gang _____

8   the witches _____   10   the sheep _____

X   There is only one correct answer.   X   There is more than one correct answer.   5

A Warm-up

Continue the sentence with two preposition phrases.

(1) Anil was left there _____

_____

(2) Anil was left there _____

_____

(3) Anil was left there _____

_____

(4) Continue the sentence using a conjunction.

Anil was left there _____

_____

Add the same prefix to make three words.

(5) _____ son   _____ corn   _____ cycle

(6) _____ cept   _____ rupt   _____ sect

(7) _____ nova   _____ highway _____ power

Add the missing letters.

(8) r h _ _ _ m

(9) _ w k w _ _ _

(10) q _ _ u e

B Word work

The same syllable is missing from both words.
Write it in.

(1) wid ____ ing   threat ____ ing

(2) mis ____ able   gen ____ ous

(3) con ____ ence   re ____ ence

Split the word to show the root word, prefix and suffix.

(4) unachievable   _____ / _____ / _____

(5) regeneration   _____ / _____ / _____

(6) unbeneficial   _____ / _____ / _____

Add a prefix and a suffix to make an adjective.

(7) ____ control ____

(8) ____ destruct ____

Circle all the words that are synonyms of each other.

(9) apply appal please horrify haul shock

(10) calm rash mild hasty reckless sane

C Sentence work

Use a parenthesis to add the information from the second sentence into the first. Write the new sentence.

(1) Michael helped David to escape. Michael is David's brother.

_____

(2) Fatima raised £1000 for the charity. She works in a bank.

_____

(3) Ben won first prize. He is aged sixteen. _____

Sort the modal verbs into two groups. **must might could can may will should shall**

(4) **show certainty** _____

(5) **show possibility** _____

Change the sentence from a certainty to a possibility. Cross out one word and write a new one.

(6) Mr Jones said that we could definitely play cricket this afternoon. _____

(7) Other people said they will help if needed. _____

Add the missing full stops, commas and capital letters.

(8) Aaron ran down the hill shouting loudly the dog ignoring me bounded after him.

(9) After two difficult years Marie then aged ten went to live with her grandmother.

(10) As the strangers came to a halt Jessica looked up her face was pale and frightened.

X There is only one correct answer.   X There is more than one correct answer.

A Warm-up

We spoke _____ .

Write two adverbs that could be used to show

1. **how** _____ _____

2. **where** _____ _____

3. **when** _____ _____

Add the missing prefix.

Clue: to do with computers

4. _____ active

5. _____ link

6. _____ media

7. Write one other word with each prefix.

_____

Underline the odd one out.

8. **possessive pronouns** ours its his there's

9. **prepositions** with at during an

10. **conjunctions** but if all until

B Word work

Add each suffix and write the new words.

ed ment

1. **equip** _____

2. **commit** _____

3. Add the same ending to both words.

consequ _____ influ _____

Add two more words with the same prefix.

4. **ex**-teacher

_____ _____

5. **semi**-conscious

_____ _____

6. Write the meaning of the prefixes.

semi- _____ **ex-** _____

Write four different definitions.

7. **beat** _____

8. **beat** _____

9. **beat** _____

10. **beat** _____

C Sentence work

Name the type of sentence and explain why the writer has used it in the title.

1. **Does the Loch Ness monster really exist?** _____ _____

2. **Act now to save the whale.** _____ _____

3. **What a show it was!** _____ _____

4. Make this statement into a question. Do it in two ways.

There is a solution. _____ _____

Rewrite the sentence so that it sounds less definite.

5. The cake will be ready on time. _____

6. In the future we will all have electric cars. _____

7. Michael used the key to escape. _____

Complete the sentence by adding a parenthesis.

8. The team _____ played well.

9. The castle _____ stands on a hill.

10. Olivia _____ found the painting.

| X There is only one correct answer. | X There is more than one correct answer. |

A Warm-up

Use the words **cat** and **bowl** in a

1. **sentence** _____

_____

2. **command** _____

_____

3. **question** _____

_____

4. **sentence with a relative clause**

_____

_____

weary polite tidy

Add the same suffix to each of the three words to make

5. **nouns** _____

6. **adverbs** _____

Add the missing letters. **Clue:** *buildings*

7. h o _ p _ t _ l

8. r e s t _ _ r _ n t

9. o b s _ _ v _ t _ ry

10. g _ m n _ s _ m

B Word work

1. Add **ie** or **ei**.

p _ _ r c e   b r _ _ f l y   r e c _ _ p t

2. What rule did you use?

_____

3. Underline the letter string in all the words.

ought trough plough thorough bough

4. Write the two words where the letter string makes the same sound.

_____ _____

Write three words related to the root word in **bold**.

5. **hero** _____

6. **just** _____

7. **know** _____

Write a definition. **Clue:** *to do with plants*

8. **germination** _____

9. **dispersal** _____

10. **pollination** _____

C Sentence work

Identify the text type. Underline the longer noun phrase at the start of the sentence.

1. The brave teenager, now resting at home, rescued her trapped friends. _____

2. Hundreds of homeless animals are in urgent need of your help – right now. _____

3. The man with the white beard stood in the quiet, moonlit square. _____

Give two ways in which the nouns in the above phrases are modified.

4. _____

5. _____

Write four modal verbs that could be used to complete the sentence.

6. He _____ be late today. _____

7. They _____ have passed us. _____

8. Put a tick if the apostrophes are used correctly. Put a cross if they are not.

Jenny's mum hadn't any money. _____   Fan's were eager to see Citys' new signing. _____

We could'nt hear the actor's dialogue. _____

Write correctly the sentences that you have put a cross beside.

9. _____

10. _____

X There is only one correct answer.   X There is more than one correct answer.

A Warm-up

Write a sentence about a new snack called choco-pops. Begin with the given determiner.

1 This _____

_____

2 An _____

_____

3 Some _____

_____

4 Every _____

_____

What word could you write in the gap to make a new word? Write two possibilities.

5 in _____ ly _____

6 un _____ ably _____

7 ir _____ ibly _____

Add the name of a household item to complete the word.

8 e n v _____ m e n t

9 o c _____ y

10 a c c o m _____ y

B Word work

Cross out the words that are wrongly spelt. Write the correct spellings.

1 The fourty soldures were incredibley brave.

_____

2 Can amatures compeat with prefessionels?

_____

Add two words with the same suffix.

3 **quarrelsome** _____

4 **toward** _____

5 **lengthwise** _____

Draw a line to match the synonyms.

6 enforce   abandon

7 desert   propose

8 suggest   impose

Underline the words that

9 can be **nouns** as well as **adjectives**

ugly annual large final busy

10 can be **nouns** as well as **verbs**

cook rely polish deliver compose

C Sentence work

Reorder the words to make three better sentences. Start each one with a different adverbial.

The king saw the statue unfortunately as he entered the castle in the evening.

1 _____

2 _____

3 _____

Cross out the words that are informal. Write new words that sound more formal.

4 They got rid of the stuff. _____

5 They got hold of the kit. _____

6 The bloke seemed a bit shady. _____

Add a pair of brackets within each sentence.

7 Some eagles build their nests called eyries on cliff tops.

8 Ned kept the two dogs Shep and Flick for many years.

9 Rob Jones the team's manager was unhappy with the decision.

10 What other punctuation could have been used instead of brackets? _____

X There is only one correct answer.   X There is more than one correct answer.

9

A   Warm-up

Use the words **football** and **cake** in a sentence with

1   **one clause** _____

_____

2   **two clauses** _____

_____

3   Join a prefix to the word to make a verb.

mis	duct
dis	lead
over	connect
de	turn

Use the words to complete these phrases.

4   _____ a cable   6   _____ points

5   _____ a boat   7   _____ people

All these compound words are to do with computers.
Complete them using

8   **adjectives**   _____ cut   _____ ware

9   **prepositions**   _____ load   _____ line

10   **nouns**   _____ bar   _____ work

B   Word work

1   Underline the root words.

outrageous prosperous rebellious

2   Which root word changes when **ous** is added?

_____ because _____

3   Complete these word sums.

medal + ist   = _____

control + able = _____

Write the word to go with the definition.
*Clue: starts with **in** or **im***

4   _____   not fixed, unclear

5   _____   unfinished

6   _____   childish

7   _____   fixed, cannot be moved

8   _____   not likely

9   _____   wrong, not exact

10   Write the longer word to use in formal writing.

fridge _____   **ref** _____

brill _____   **veg** _____

C   Sentence work

Underline the main clause.

1   He waited for hours as the rain fell.

2   I enjoyed the game even though we lost.

Rewrite 1 and 2 above with the subordinate clause at the start.

3   _____

4   _____

Extend and improve the sentence. Include a relative clause.

5   A wizard sped down the street.

_____

6   The little girl heard footsteps.

_____

7   He saw a face.

_____

Add a colon and continue the sentence with a list.

8   We divide the year up into four seasons _____

9   Abby checked her pockets _____

10   For this trick you need a few simple objects _____

X There is only one correct answer.   X There is more than one correct answer.

A Warm-up

Read the headline. Then write the first sentence of the article including a subordinate clause.

1 **United on cloud nine** _____

_____

_____

2 **Thief caught red-handed** _____

_____

_____

Write two words related to the word in **bold**.

3 **apology** _____

4 **mystery** _____

5 **apply** _____

6 **calculate** _____

7 Make six verbs by adding prefixes to **act** and **do**.

_____

_____

Add a short word to complete the longer word.

8 m e a _____ m e n t   10 a c _____ i n g l y

9 d i s a p _____ e d

B Word work

Add the suffixes to each root word to make three new words.

ing ed ence

1 refer _____   refer _____   refer _____

2 confer _____   confer _____   confer _____

3 prefer _____   prefer _____   prefer _____

4 Underline the word that should have a hyphen.

reassure reenter reboot refill refuel

Add the correct prefix.

5 The footballer signed a new _____ tract.

6 I can _____ tract him while you escape.

7 Nothing will _____ tract from her success.

Write a definition.

8 **pitch** (in music) _____

9 **pitch** (in sport) _____

10 **pitch** (in camping) _____

C Sentence work

Combine the three sentences into one. Do it in four different ways.

It was still snowing. Amy rushed outside. She made a snowman.

1 _____

2 _____

3 _____

4 _____

Write three alternatives for the word in **bold**. They do not have to be synonyms.

5 **The** people were shouting. _____

6 The dog was **on** the table. _____

7 Write the name of the class of words that you used

in Q5: _____   **in Q6:** _____

Draw a line to the name of the punctuation mark used between the clauses.

8 That morning, I was very late; Ben had already left.   colon

9 We were delighted: the party had been a success.   comma

10 When I eventually arrived, it was too late.   semi-colon

X There is only one correct answer.   X There is more than one correct answer.

11

A Warm-up

Reorder the words to make three different sentences.

was Jake sitting there beside her

1 _____

2 _____

3 _____

Underline the possessive pronoun that is hidden in each word.

4 determined   5 profits

Underline the preposition that is hidden in each word.

6 ordinary   7 recovery

Write an adverb using the word in **bold**.

8 **probable** _____

9 **possible** _____

10 Underline the verb to which you can add all these prefixes.

re im dis

claim cover prove press

B Word work

Add the missing syllables.

1 con / _____ / ver / _____
Clue: strong disagreement about an issue

2 ap / _____ / hen / _____
Clue: anxious

3 op / _____ / tu / _____ / ty
Clue: a chance to do something

4 _____ / lu / _____ / _____
Clue: light up

Write a noun and an adjective related to the verb.

5 **create** _____

6 **vary** _____

7 **imagine** _____

Write a definition.
Clue: found in a book about the Moon

8 **weightlessness** _____

9 **uninhabitable** _____

10 **spherical** _____

C Sentence work

Add the missing punctuation.

1 Simon turned it was the same voice yes there was the mysterious stranger

2 There was a crash Stella jumped she clutched the chair waiting

Add a subject and an object to complete the sentence.

3 _____ dropped _____   4 _____ caught _____

Write three adverbials that could be used

5 **to show a result** _____

6 **to add more information** _____

7 **to put a different view** _____

Continue the sentence with a simile or a metaphor that creates a feeling of

8 **panic**   The crowd _____

9 **calm**   The wind _____

10 **excitement** The acrobat _____

X There is only one correct answer.   X There is more than one correct answer.

A Warm-up

The Tardis has disappeared.

Write the next three sentences.

(1) **an exclamation** _____

_____

(2) **a question** _____

_____

(3) **a possibility** _____

_____

_____

The ending of the word is missing. Write two suggestions as to what the complete word might be.

(4) i l l u _____   _____

(5) i m m e _____   _____

(6) i r r e _____   _____

Write two words related to the word in **bold**.

(7) **perform** _____

(8) **drama** _____

(9) **idea** _____

(10) **assist** _____

B Word work

Add the same ending to all three words.

ery ary ory

(1) diction _____   prim _____   ordin _____

(2) gall _____   lott _____   cemet _____

(3) categ _____   fact _____   direct _____

(4) Make four words using these word parts only.

graph auto bio y logy

_____

_____

Write the meaning of the word part.

(5) **auto** _____ (7) **bio** _____

(6) **graph** _____ (8) **logy** _____

(9) Draw a line to match the antonyms.

dependable   unnecessary

adequate   unreliable

required   insufficient

(10) Underline the two synonyms.

havoc haven harmony disorder distinct

C Sentence work

Add a subordinate clause that gives a contrasting idea. Use a different conjunction each time.

(1) Some believe that the fire was caused deliberately _____

(2) Hannah was trembling _____

(3) They continued to struggle _____

(4) City had the better first half, _____

(5) Underline the subject of this sentence.   Fire destroyed acres of woodland.

(6) Underline the object of this sentence.   Fire fighters fought the fire.

(7) Write a sentence using the word **flames** as the

subject _____   **object** _____

Continue the sentence after the punctuation mark.

(8) Many objects are made from wood: _____

(9) The rock is very porous (_____

(10) The door slammed – _____

A Warm-up

1 Write a two-clause sentence using these words.

book hair pencil

_____

_____

Write two three-syllable words with the ending given.

2 **ture** _____ _____

3 **sure** _____ _____

4 **sion** _____ _____

5 **tial** _____ _____

Write the suffix that makes all the words into verbs.

6 sharp tight bright deep light _____

7 idol equal final organ civil _____

Complete the simile.

8 as springy as _____

9 as welcome as _____

10 as silent as _____

B Word work

Add the correct ending to the adjectives.

1 transpar _____

2 toler _____

3 eleg _____

4 conveni _____

Write a noun related to the word in **bold**.

5 **confer** _____

6 **infer** _____

Write an adjective related to the word in **bold**.

7 **courage** _____

8 **recharge** _____

Write a more formal synonym for the word in **bold**.

9 It was **wrecked**. _____

10 We **ditched** it. _____

C Sentence work

Is the sentence active or passive? Write your answer.

1 The case was closed. _____

2 A stranger opened the door. _____

3 Rain destroyed the crops. _____

Rewrite the active sentences as passive sentences.

4 _____   5 _____

Continue the sentence so that it builds up suspense. Add a subordinate and a main clause.

6 I followed the path _____

_____

Write two short contrasting sentences to follow the long one that you have just written.

7 _____   8 _____

Punctuate the extract.

9 Charlie now aged 92 remembers Ilford as it was There was Wilsons dairy he recalls

10 Julia Hopkins who judged the competition said Nikkis poster is really eye catching

X There is only one correct answer.   X There is more than one correct answer.

A Warm-up

Write a pun based on the homophones.

1 **hair/hare** _____

_____

2 **right/write** _____

_____

3 **sent/scent** _____

_____

4 **you/ewe** _____

_____

Underline the words that do **not** have
a plural form.

5 child furniture goose advice

Use the word **charge** as a

6 **noun** _____

7 **verb** _____

Add the same prefix to all three words.

8 ____ fault   ____ flate   ____ compose

9 ____ owner   ____ driver   ____ star

10 ____ large   ____ grave   ____ trust

B Word work

Cross out the words that are wrongly spelt.
Write the correct spellings.

1 I made freequent jurneys to foregn lands.

_____

2 I past many familier towns in the reegon.

_____

3 I recergnised many ansient structchers.

_____

Underline the root and write its meaning.

4 popular population populate

_____

5 pedal pedestrian pedometer

_____

6 aeroplane aerospace aerosol

_____

7 prime primary primrose

_____

Write two synonyms to use in formal writing.

8 **plus** _____

9 **so** _____

10 **then again** _____

C Sentence work

Rewrite the sentence in the passive voice.

1 City won the game. _____

2 The mayor presented the prize. _____

3 Jaguar made the car in 1961. _____

4 The waves splashed the spectators. _____

The old lady glared at the boy.

Add more detail to this sentence by adding

5 **a relative clause** _____

6 **a parenthesis** _____

7 **another main clause** _____

Punctuate the sentence by adding a comma and a dash.

8 Although desperate to finish he couldn't walk any further the pain was too bad.

9 If you want the best try Zoom trainers they're great!

10 When he heard this Joe began to laugh he knew the truth at last.

Now complete Section 1 of the Progress chart on page 46.

X There is only one correct answer.   X There is more than one correct answer.

15

The happening

Read the first line of the story, as given in the box below. Write the next part of the story.

Hints

Before you start:

- think about the type of your story (for example, it could be a fantasy, adventure or realistic story)
- think about similar stories you have read and what makes them effective
- decide how you will develop the main character of David
- decide on a setting and how this might contribute to the atmosphere
- plan the events of your story so they develop to an interesting ending.

As you write:

- think about your audience and how to tell the story effectively
- think carefully as you choose words and grammatical features that will enhance the effect.

David woke up. He knew immediately that something strange had happened.

Continue on a separate sheet if necessary.

Check

- When you have finished, check through your writing. Make changes to clarify meaning or enhance the effect.
- Check that everything is grammatically correct.
- Proofread to check spelling and punctuation.

Flood alert

Proofread this radio news report.

Change anything that does not look or sound correct.

Hints

- Check that everything is clear and sounds right.
- Check that the punctuation has been used correctly and effectively.
- Check that the spelling is correct.

All day water levels have continyued to rise threatning many homes.

Mr Jackson the chief flood officer said of coarse, many people are feeling anxtious. And we are offerring advise and assistence wherever possable."

The floods have also caused caos across the transport sistem. Earlier today police called the roads 'trecherus' and said that people aught to remain in their homes some drivers cars were underwater.

Eric Brown an expolice officer who lives in the village told us he could not believe how quickly the water rose. He said we're just relieved to be safe.

Even though there has been torrenshal rain for sevarel days it seems people recieved no offisial warning.

Acording to weather forcasters more rain is expected this evening so the situation could possibley worsen.

Extra

Imagine that you are to present a radio news report about a hurricane that hit your area last night.
On a separate sheet of paper, write the beginning of your report.

A Warm-up

Rewrite the sentence. Use more interesting nouns and verbs and add an extra detail.

1   The woman gets out of the car.

_____

_____

2   The dog looked at the man.

_____

_____

3   The man came into the room.

_____

_____

Add one letter to make a grammar term.

4   smile   _____

5   cause   _____

6   phase   _____

7   nun   _____

Write two nouns related to the word in **bold**.

8   **destroy**   _____

9   **apply**   _____

10   **equal**   _____

B Word work

Add a prefix and/or suffix to complete the words.

1   script _____   script _____   script _____

2   verb _____   verb _____   verb _____

3   part _____   part _____   part _____

Write the correct spelling of the underlined word.

4   much <u>resistence</u>   _____

5   a <u>dorment</u> volcano   _____

6   a strange <u>substence</u>   _____

7   a good <u>influance</u>   _____

Write a definition of the word in **bold**.

8   the **seabed**

_____

_____

9   the cube's **volume**

_____

_____

10   a **litter** of three

_____

C Sentence work

Rewrite the information as a single sentence with a relative clause. Do it in two different ways.

Oxygen is a gas. It is found in the air. It is essential to life.

1   _____

2   _____

3   Why do the single sentences sound better?   _____

Rewrite the sentence, adding a preposition phrase to modify the subject of the sentence.

4   The cat chased the mouse.   _____

5   The man saw the accident.   _____

6   The birds ate the seeds.   _____

One day almost five years later the man returned.

Punctuate the sentence using

7   **commas**   _____

8   **brackets**   _____

9   **dashes**   _____

10   What are the different effects of these punctuation marks?   _____

X There is only one correct answer.   X There is more than one correct answer.

A Warm-up

Add three adverbs to make a sentence that says **when**, **how** and **where**.

1 _____ it rained

_____ .

2 _____ we played

_____ .

3 The man _____

waits _____ .

Make a word that ends and a word that starts with each letter string.

4 _____ gy ➔ gy _____

5 _____ cy ➔ cy _____

6 _____ phy ➔ phy _____

Write a sentence using the homophones.

7 **herd/heard** _____

8 **whale/wail** _____

9 **dear/deer** _____

10 **steel/steal** _____

B Word work

Write the adjective related to the noun.

1 **nutrition** _____

2 **suspicion** _____

Write the verb and noun related to the word in **bold**.

3 **insistent** _____ _____

4 **defiant** _____ _____

Add the missing syllables.

5 im / _____ / _____ / _____ / ly
   Clue: straightaway

6 ap / _____ / _____ / _____ / ly
   Clue: roughly, about

7 ap / _____ / _____ / ly
   Clue: seemingly

Write a synonym for the word in **bold**.

8 It was a **difficult** journey. _____

9 It is a **difficult** problem. _____

10 He can be **difficult**. _____

C Sentence work

Complete the sentence using these words. Circle the main clause in the sentence.

orange football

1 Although _____

2 After _____

3 As _____

What a mess it was! You wouldn't believe it. Norma's cottage? More like Nor-mess cottage!

4 Underline the word that best describes the style of this text.   formal traditional informal

Give three reasons to explain your choice.

5 _____

6 _____

7 _____

Add the comma or commas needed to make the meaning of the sentence clear.

8 Have you tried jogging before Emma?

9 Giraffes which have long necks can reach food from tall trees.

10 According to Bharat James is often late.

A Warm-up

Use the words **pigeon** and **wall** in a sentence using

1 **a parenthesis** _____

_____

2 **two main clauses** _____

_____

3 **a conjunction** _____

_____

Complete the mnemonic, which helps you to spell the word at the end of the sentence.

4 You find a _____ in an acci _____ .

5 There is a _____ in sepa _____ e.

6 Put a _____ in a com _____ ition.

7 Find out who _____ in a ce _____ ery.

Write two words related to the word in **bold**.

8 **identity** _____

9 **belief** _____

10 **human** _____

B Word work

Write the word to go with the definition.
The word begins with one of these prefixes.

il im ir

1 _____ unlikely

2 _____ a false idea

3 _____ cannot be changed back or undone

Add **ei** or **ie** to make the long **ee** sound.

4 d e c _ t y _ l d s _ z e

5 r e l _ v e s _ g e p r o t _ n

6 Which two words in questions 4 and 5 do **not** follow the normal 'i before e' rule?

_____

Write a more formal synonym for the word in **bold**.

7 Leave your **stuff** here. _____

8 It was **okay**. _____

9 They **put up** the price. _____

10 Knock before you **go in**. _____

C Sentence work

Complete the sentence so that it follows this one.

Rays from the sun can be harmful.

1 For example, _____

2 Furthermore, _____

3 As a result, _____

4 However, _____

Cross out the verb. Change it to the present perfect form.

5 We are holding _____ talks with the shop's owner.

6 The plants are beginning _____ to grow.

7 The wind is doing _____ a lot of damage.

8 Miss Hawkins is teaching _____ us about plants.

Add three more noun phrases to the list.

9 The room was full of treasure: necklaces of glistening stones; rings with _____

10 He created a sumptuous feast: plates of roasted meats; steaming _____

X There is only one correct answer.   X There is more than one correct answer.

A Warm-up

Rewrite the sentence, changing the word order.

A figure appeared slowly, as the mist faded.

1 _____

2 _____

3 _____

Write a word with the ending given.

4 **ion** _____

5 **cious** _____

6 **tious** _____

Add a subject and an object.

7 _____ wrote _____

8 _____ packed _____

9 _____ caught _____

10 _____ drank _____

B Word work

Write sentences using the word **just** as an

1 **adverb** _____

2 **adjective** _____

3 Add suffixes to make **just** into a

verb _____

noun _____

4 Write three more words related to the word **just**.

_____ _____ _____

Add the silent letter.

5 _ n i g h t   _ n e a d   _ n a v e

6 _ r e a t h   _ r e n c h   _ r a t h

7 a u t u m _   h y m _   c o l u m _

8 l a m _   l i m _   n u m _

Write three words that end with the letters in **bold**.

9 **clude** _____

10 **gram** _____

C Sentence work

Rewrite the sentence in the passive voice.

1 A security man guarded the painting. _____

2 Dr Gill organised the competition. _____

3 The mud ruined her shoes. _____

4 The emperor saved the kingdom. _____

5 How is the passive version different? _____

Continue the sentence with a relative clause. Create a different mood in each sentence.

6 He came to a room _____

7 He came to a room _____

Punctuate the sentences. Use different punctuation marks in each one.

8 It seemed to me or perhaps I imagined it that the old man smiled.

9 If she fails as I think she will we must go on alone.

10 The planets orbit travel round the Sun.

A Warm-up

Use the words **car** and **tree** in a sentence using

1 **the active voice**

2 **the passive voice**

3 **a conjunction**

4 **a relative clause**

Make a word that ends and a word that starts
with each letter string.

5 _____ **gue** ➔ **gue** _____

6 _____ **gn** ➔ **gn** _____

7 _____ **que** ➔ **que** _____

Complete the spelling of the linking adverb.

8 **c o n s** _____ *Clue: as a result*

9 **s u b s** _____ *Clue: afterwards*

10 **i n i** _____ *Clue: at first*

B Word work

1 Add the correct prefix.

post pre

_____ caution _____ script _____ cede

Write the meaning of the prefix.

2 **pre** _____ 3 **post** _____

Add **able** or **ible**.

4 **vis** _____ **detest** _____ **resist** _____

5 **formid** _____ **accept** _____ **aud** _____

Which two words above do **not** follow the usual
able/ible pattern?

6 _____ 7 _____

8 What is the normal rule for adding **able**
and **ible**?

Write a definition of the well-known saying.

9 **in the limelight** _____

10 **to be given the sack** _____

C Sentence work

Ravi waited by the door.

Rewrite the sentence, adding a subordinate clause to the

1 **beginning**

2 **middle**

3 **end**

Does the text sound formal or informal?

4 Anita was born in 1948 in King's Norton, part of Birmingham. _____

5 Just in from college. What a day it was! _____

Give two features used in the informal text that are not found in formal writing.

6 _____ 7 _____

Add a colon and complete the sentence.

8 He couldn't read the letter

9 She read the address on the note

10 Evie read the opening words

X There is only one correct answer. X There is more than one correct answer.

A Warm-up

Continue the sentence after the conjunction.

1. The clown danced even though _____

_____

2. The clown danced as if _____

_____

3. The clown danced whenever _____

_____

Add a suffix to make the word into a verb.

4. crystal _____
5. beauty _____
6. critic _____
7. identity _____

Put the letters in order to make a word.

8. **o g h u t** _____
9. **o g u h c** _____
10. **o g h t u f** _____

B Word work

Add the ending to complete the adverb.

1. consider _____ *Clue: very much*
2. notice _____ *Clue: quite clearly*
3. incred _____ *Clue: amazingly*

Complete the word sum.

4. **curious** + **ity** = _____
5. **generous** + **ity** = _____
6. **vapour** + **ise** = _____
7. **glamour** + **ise** = _____

8. Explain why these words do not follow usual spelling rules.

_____

_____

Write a definition.

9. **metre** (in maths) _____

_____

10. **metre** (in poetry) _____

C Sentence work

Rewrite the sentence with the adverbial at the beginning.

1. He stepped onto the stage despite his nerves. _____
2. The door opened as she stood there weeping. _____
3. What is the effect of reordering the sentences? _____

The door opened.

Rewrite the sentence as a multi-clause sentence with detail to match the story type.

4. **school story** _____
5. **mystery** _____
6. **sci-fi** _____

Why are the punctuation marks needed in the sentence?

Phoebe is now my ex-best friend – I mean it this time.

7. **hyphen** _____
8. **dash** _____

Em says it's my fault (but she would say that, wouldn't she?).

9. **comma** _____
10. **apostrophes** _____

X There is only one correct answer.   X There is more than one correct answer.

A Warm-up

Cross out the noun and complete the simile with an interesting and original noun phrase.

① as white as snow

_____

② as quiet as a mouse

_____

③ as deep as the sea

_____

Write in full the word that the short form stands for.

④ **ID** _____

⑤ **pro** _____

⑥ **ad** _____

⑦ **demo** _____

Write the missing letters.
***Clue:** small books*

⑧ b r o _____

⑨ p a m _____

⑩ c a t _____

B Word work

Add the same ending to make three nouns.

① accept _____ guide _____ ignore _____

② insist _____ exis _____ occur _____

Change the ending on the adjective to write the related noun.

③ **frequent** _____

④ **vacant** _____

⑤ Add a short word to complete the longer word.

c o m _____ y   e m _____ r a s s

e n v _____ m e n t   v e _____ a b l e

⑥ Write the word correctly.

thisle _____   doutful _____

Add the same word to complete both figures of speech.

⑦ in _____ pursuit; too _____ to handle

⑧ the _____ is on; in the _____ of the moment

⑨ out _____ ; make your blood run _____

⑩ a _____ customer; keep your _____

C Sentence work

Complete the subordinate clause to add a condition.

① The sponsored walk will go ahead on Friday unless _____

② People would not drop litter if _____

③ Martin will be able to come, provided that _____

④ They will be here soon, so long as _____

Write a one-sentence summary of the story that includes a subordinate clause.

⑤ **Cinderella** _____

⑥ **Goldilocks** _____

⑦ **Robin Hood** _____

Add a semi-colon.

⑧ There was no choice we had to leave.

⑨ The house was empty nothing stirred.

⑩ Don't interrupt I haven't finished.

X There is only one correct answer.   X There is more than one correct answer.

A Warm-up

Write a question-and-answer joke based on the homonym.

1 **trunk** _____

_____

2 **wave** _____

_____

3 **watch** _____

_____

Add the same short word to complete both longer words.

4 d e s _____ a t i o n   e x _____ g u i s h

5 l i s _____ e d   g l i s _____ e d

6 f o _____   s o v e _____

7 g r a _____   i n d i v i _____

Add the missing letters.
Clue: story types

8 m _ s t _ r _____

9 s _____ c e f i c _____

10 _ d v _ n _____

B Word work

Add a word to complete each compound word.
Clue: conjunctions

1 _____ fore

2 hence _____

3 _____ theless

4 _____ over

5 Underline the prefix in each word.

dissolve conscience correspond accompany

6 How does this help to spell the word correctly?

_____

_____

7 Add the silent letter. **b p**

de _ t   r e c e i _ t

p l u m _ i n g   _ s a l m

Write a modern phrase that means the same.

8 **set forth** _____

9 **yonder** _____

10 **go thither** _____

C Sentence work

Rewrite the sentence in the passive voice without mentioning the person or people responsible.

1 Jasper slew the dragon. _____

2 The people sent a message. _____

3 A servant had broken the mirror. _____

4 The postman had delivered the letter. _____

Complete the table with words and phrases used in formal and informal letters.

	formal	informal
5	domestic residence	
6		Hi!
7	in duplicate	

Why has the colon been used?

8 There are three events: the sprint, long jump and high jump. _____

9 He read the words on the sign: Harborough Hall. _____

10 He knew he was late: it was past nine o'clock. _____

X There is only one correct answer.   X There is more than one correct answer.

A Warm-up

Write the next three sentences.

Harry slipped and fell into the mud.

1 As a result, _____

_____

2 Unfortunately, _____

_____

3 However, _____

_____

Underline the word that **cannot** be a verb.

4 book float ring planet bat

5 pop spot safe snap bubble

6 light lead year note ferry

Add the missing letters.

7 m _ th _ lo _ y

8 m _ st _ fy

9 h _ pn _ t _ st

10 _ _ m _ etric _ l

B Word work

1 Add the correct prefix. **sub anti micro**

_____ freeze   _____ dote   _____ biotic

_____ chip   _____ -organism

_____ merge   _____ zero   _____ terranean

Write the meaning of the prefix.

2 **anti** _____

3 **micro** _____

4 **sub** _____

5 Add the same two letters to all the words.

m a _ i n e r y   h e a d a _ e

a r _ i t e c t   p a r a _ u t e

6 Add the missing letter.

e x _ i b i t i o n   v e _ i c l e

s i l _ o u e t t e

Write a synonym for the word in **bold**.

7 Tigers **follow** their prey. _____

8 Police **follow** criminals. _____

9 **Follow** the rules. _____

10 I couldn't **follow** the story. _____

C Sentence work

Rewrite the sentence, adding two commas. Explain how the commas change the meaning.

1 The puppies which were brown soon found new homes.

_____

2 The sentence now means _____

3 The children who were excited waited outside.

_____

4 The sentence now means _____

Complete the verb table to show the past, past progressive and past perfect forms of the verbs.

5	eat	ate		had eaten
6	go		was going	
7	take			
8	blow			

9 Complete the sentence using fewer than 10 words: **Falling** _____

10 Complete the sentence using more than 20 words: **As Ruby** _____

X There is only one correct answer.   X There is more than one correct answer.

A   Warm-up

Add another clause to develop the idea. Do this in four different ways.

Jo was holding the key.

1 _____

2 _____

3 _____

4 _____

Write two words that end with

5 **eous** _____

6 **ious** _____

Write the antonym.

7 **future** _____

8 **prefix** _____

9 **antonym** _____

10 **formal** _____

B   Word work

Write the common root and its meaning.

1 **astronaut astronomer asterisk**

_____

2 **monorail monocle monologue**

_____

Write the noun formed by adding **ance**.

3 **appear** _____ **endure** _____

4 **hinder** _____ **enter** _____

5 Why are the spellings of the words in question 4 different?

_____

_____

6 Add the ending that makes these words into nouns.

correspond _____ **excel** _____

Write the meaning of the formal word.

7 **endorse** _____

8 **pursue** _____

9 **cease** _____

10 **commence** _____

C   Sentence work

Why has the writer used the passive voice?

1 The temperature was taken every hour. _____

2 The poor man had been robbed. _____

3 The cloak had been cut to ribbons. _____

Use personification to complete the sentence.

4 The sun _____

5 The sea _____

6 The car _____

7 The river _____

Punctuate the sentence using commas and a single dash.

8 There carved into the wood was a number the number 1004.

9 Flinging open the door he ran desperately he ran.

10 It was an amazing sight the spitting hissing serpent with its staring eyes and open jaws was slithering across the ground.

X There is only one correct answer.   X There is more than one correct answer.

A Warm-up

Complete the sentence using a metaphor or personification.

1 Daisies _____

_____

2 An aeroplane _____

_____

3 Spring _____

_____

Complete the table.

	adjective	noun	verb
4	real		
5		vision	
6			socialise

Add the missing letters.
Clue: sources of information

7 d i c _ _ _ n _ _ _

8 b _ b _ _ _ g r _ _ _ y

9 e n c _ _ _ _ p _ d _ _

10 _ _ _ _ s _ r u s

B Word work

1 Add the correct ending. **logy phobia athlon**

dec _____   bio _____   tri _____

hydro _____   zoo _____   claustro _____

Draw a line to join the root to its meaning.

2 athlon   fear of

3 logy   contest

4 phobia   the study of

Add the missing vowels.

5 b e n _ f _ c _ _ l   6 s e c r _ t _ ry

Underline the root.

7 **signal signature signpost unsigned**

8 Write the words in which the **g** is silent.

_____

Explain the meaning of the proverb.

9 Don't count your chickens before they are hatched.

_____

10 A fool and his riches are soon parted.

_____

_____

C Sentence work

Add a subordinate clause that gives a condition.

1 I could borrow the bike _____

2 He would be safe _____

3 The team would score more goals _____

4 You too can be a star player _____

Write the past perfect form of the underlined verb.

5 No rain <u>fell</u> for many weeks; the ground was parched. _____

6 The crops <u>failed</u> and the people were starving. _____

7 Explain why the past perfect form is used in these sentences.

_____

Cross out the conjunction and replace it with a semi-colon.

8 Spring is nearly here so buds will soon appear on the trees.

9 They whispered quickly because there was not much time.

10 The light went out therefore she could see nothing.

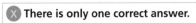 X There is only one correct answer.   X There is more than one correct answer.

A Warm-up

Make the statement into a question.

1. It's a lovely day today _____

2. You will try again _____

Dad failed his driving test three times.

Write the next two sentences. Use a linking adverbial in each.

3. _____

4. _____
   _____

Underline the word that is **not** linked by meaning.

5. bicycle binoculars biography biceps

6. decade decimal December declare

Add the missing letters.
Clue: occupations

7. p l u __ __ e r

8. o p t i __ __ __ n

9. s e c r __ __ __ r y

10. m e c __ __ n __ c

B Word work

Add the missing letters.

1. e n v i r __ __ __ m e n t

2. g o v __ __ __ m e n t

3. p a r l __ __ __ m e n t

4. s o c __ __ t y

5. Add the correct word ending.

   ency ancy

   emerg _____   hesit _____   frequ _____

Write two words formed from the root word.

6. **music** _____

7. **moist** _____

8. **mobile** _____

Write a modern word or phrase that means the same.

9. **pauper** _____

10. **wireless** _____

C Sentence work

Complete the sentence.

1. Limping _____

2. Frightened _____

3. Leaping _____

4. Holding _____

We like skateboarding so I guess a skateboard park would be great.

5. Underline the words that make this sentence sound personal and informal.

6. Rewrite the sentence to make it sound impersonal and formal.

   _____

7. When might you use the formal version? _____

Punctuate the sentence.

8. Suddenly, there was a loud scream everyone leapt to their feet.

9. A word of warning don't try this at home

10. At that moment we realised there was no going back it was too late

Now complete Section 2 of the Progress chart on page 46.

X There is only one correct answer.   X There is more than one correct answer.

Moving day

Dan and Megan's family are moving from the city to live in the country. Megan is pleased about the move; her brother Dan is not. Write separate entries for Dan and Megan for the day they arrive at their new home.

Hints

Before you start:

• consider what might have happened on moving day

• decide how you will develop the two contrasting characters

• think about diaries, their purpose, what they contain and the tone.

As you write:

• remember to use a suitable style for a personal diary

• think carefully about the words you choose and how you express ideas

• try out sentences to see if they sound convincing.

Dan's diary	Megan's diary

Continue on a separate sheet if necessary.

Check

• When you have finished, check through your writing. Make changes to clarify meaning or enhance the effect.

• Check that everything is grammatically correct.

• Proofread to check spelling and punctuation.

The rainforest

Proofread these two texts, which are in different styles.
Change anything that does not look or sound correct.

Hints

- Check that everything is clear and sounds right.
- Check that the punctuation has been used correctly and effectively.
- Check that the spelling is correct.

Factual description

The rainforest is a very spesial envirament a preshous natural habitat that is home to a vareity of truely remarkible plant's and animals.

Wherever light reaches the forest floor ecxotic ferns flurish. While high above the trees branches form a cannopy of leaves and flowers which is home to millions of curius insects and animals. The trees provide these incredable creatures with a essenshal supply of food fruits nuts seeds and polen.

Poetic description

Trees of dizzying hieght tangle together forming a secret garden not visable from below amongst elegent colums of greenery brightly coloured flowers intwine branches with their mouth's open to the insistant rain.

Only tiny chinks of light and the drip of rain can peirce the darkness of the forest cieling. Here roots hang like ropes from anceint bells.

Extra

On a separate sheet of paper, write a brief poetic piece about your garden, local park or school grounds. Choose your words carefully. Include at least one simile and one metaphor.

SECTION 3 | Test 1

A Warm-up

Complete the subordinate clause.

1 Jemma is happy as long as _____

2 Jemma is happy until _____

3 Jemma is happy while _____

4 Jemma is happy although _____

Add the missing letters.

5 c h a m _____ n
6 c h a m _____ e
7 c h a m _____ n
8 c h a n _____ r

Explain the derivation.

9 **hyperlink** comes from _____

10 **cyber café** comes from _____

B Word work

Write the correct spelling.

1 comunication _____

2 prononsiation _____

3 exagaration _____

Write two words that start with the prefix.

4 **mal** _____

5 **multi** _____

6 Write the meaning of the prefix.

mal _____

multi _____

Write different definitions of each noun.

7 **rap** _____

8 **rap** _____

9 **cricket** _____

10 **cricket** _____

C Sentence work

Rewrite the sentence so that the information given in brackets is included as a parenthesis.

1 The gerbil is best suited to life in the desert. (UK – popular pet) _____

2 Birds of prey include hawks and owls. (hawks hunt – day; owls hunt – night) _____

3 Edward Jenner pioneered vaccination. (b. 1749; a doctor) _____

Write the formal sentence so that it sounds informal.

4 I am completely blameless. _____

5 Refrain from conversing. _____

Write the informal sentence so that it sounds formal.

6 You shouldn't do things like that. _____

7 Sorry I can't help you. _____

Write a sentence with direct speech to open the traditional story.

8 **Red Riding Hood** _____

9 **Snow White** _____

10 **Aladdin** _____

X There is only one correct answer.   X There is more than one correct answer.

A Warm-up

Write a sentence using the word **spell** as a

1 **verb** _____

_____

2 **noun** _____

_____

Write a sentence using the word **caterpillars** as the

3 **subject** _____

4 **object** _____

Add the missing letters.

5 a p p r e _____ a t e
6 f e r o _____ s
7 a r t i f i _____ l
8 e f f i _____ n t

Make three words.

9 **auto tele cue gram graph**

_____

10 **med graph para ic al**

_____

B Word work

Complete the word to go with the definition.
Use a dictionary to check the spelling.

1 a n t _____ expect to happen

2 a n t _____ collection of poems or stories

3 a n t _____ dislike; hostility

4 a n t _____ aerial; one of the feelers on an insect

5 These words and prefixes are mixed up. Write them correctly.

webport **heli**lung **aqua**cam

_____

Write a more formal synonym.

6 **try** _____

7 **watch over** _____

8 **ask for** _____

9 **turn down** _____

10 **go ahead** _____

C Sentence work

Complete the sentence.

1 Hiding _____

2 Balanced _____

3 Peering _____

4 Surprised _____

Edit the sentence. Cross out any repeated or unnecessary words.

5 He tried parachuting because he had always wanted to try parachuting.

6 Mix the yeast into the flour and then add water to the flour.

7 The ship was pounded by enormous waves and finally the ship sank.

Use brackets to add a parenthesis giving extra explanation or examples.

8 Icebergs are formed when glaciers _____ meet the sea.

9 Bread, pasta _____ and some cereals are made from wheat.

10 Different types of figurative language _____ are used to create a mood or feeling.

X There is only one correct answer.   X There is more than one correct answer.

A Warm-up

Write an advert for **Sam's soups** using features of informal writing.

1. **a contraction** _____

2. **an exclamation** _____
   _____

3. **a question tag** _____
   _____

4. **informal words** _____
   _____

Add the missing letters. *Clue: types of boat*

5. y _ _ t

6. d i n _ _ _

7. c a n _ _

Write the prefix that can be added to all three words.

8. final colon circle _____

9. natural structure human _____

10. hang power load _____

B Word work

Add the same ending to all three words.

ary ery ory

1. direct ____   categ ____   dormit ____

2. rot ____   volunt ____   tribut ____

3. scen ____   jewell ____   machin ____

4. Complete the word to go with the definition.

   ball ____   a song or poem

   ball ____   a type of dance

   ball ____   a vote

Read the words you made in question 4. Write the words that are derived from each meaning of the word **ball**. Use a dictionary to help you.

5. **ball** a dance _____

6. **ball** a round object _____

7. Write three words starting with the root **aero**.
   _____

Cross out the incorrect words in the phrase.

8. a weather **vein vane vain**

9. a **stationary stationery** shop

10. a steep **descent dissent decent**

C Sentence work

Rewrite the sentence in the active voice to focus on the main character.

1. A sudden scream startled him. _____

2. The swirling lights dazzled her. _____

3. The man's strange clothing puzzled me. _____

4. The sound of the sea calmed Ellie's mind. _____

Improve the sentence. Add one or two adverbs for emphasis.

5. This is _____ vital.

6. This creature is now _____ rare.

7. Safety _____ is a big concern.

Add a colon and complete the sentence.

8. There are five vowels _____

9. These are examples of conjunctions _____

10. The room was now completely empty _____

X There is only one correct answer.   X There is more than one correct answer.

A Warm-up

Complete the sentence with a relative clause.

1 There is a faraway kingdom where _____

_____

2 We went to a party where _____

_____

3 I remember the day when _____

_____

Change one letter to make a homophone.

4 course _____

5 current _____

6 dual _____

7 Write in the missing animal.

That's put the _____ among the pigeons.

Write a synonym for the word in **bold**. You can use a thesaurus.

8 The ground is **soggy**. _____

9 I like **soft** colours. _____

10 It is a **stupid** idea. _____

B Word work

Write the correct spelling of the animal group.
You can use a dictionary.

1 verterbrate _____

2 amphibion _____

3 mammel _____

Use a suffix to make the noun into an adjective.

4 **triangle** _____

5 **geometry** _____

6 **cylinder** _____

Write different definitions of each word.

7 **grate** (noun) _____

8 **grate** (verb) _____

9 **hide** (noun) _____

10 **hide** (verb) _____

C Sentence work

Reorder the sentence so that it starts with the adverbial and focuses on the feelings of the character.

1 He walked on although he was scared. _____

2 They followed the others, as if in a trance. _____

3 Ed crawled into the cave despite the pain. _____

4 He stood up with a tingle of excitement. _____

5 Write three phrases that introduce one side of an argument.

_____

6 Write three phrases that introduce a different opinion.

_____

7 Write three adverbials that introduce an opposing view.

_____

Tick the sentence using a hyphen correctly.

8 Draw twenty-two dimensional shapes. ____   Draw twenty two-dimensional shapes. ____

9 The deckchair was red-hot from the sun. ____   The deck-chair was red hot from the sun. ____

10 She is a well known film-star. ____   She is a well-known film star. ____

A Warm-up

Use the words **goat** and **socks** in a sentence using the

1 **active voice** _____

_____

2 **passive voice** _____

_____

3 **perfect tense** _____

_____

Add the ending of the adjective.

4 torren _____   6 substan _____

5 atro _____   7 cons _____

Write a headline using a pun based on the homophones.

8 **main/mane** _____

_____

9 **not/knot** _____

_____

10 **aloud/allowed** _____

_____

B Word work

Add the same ending to all three words. **cial tial**

1 essen _____   poten _____   influen _____

2 benefi _____   artifi _____   finan _____

Add the silent letter.

b g h n s t

3 solem _ n   i _ le   campai _ n

4 hus _ le   ex _ ibit   su _ tle

Add a different prefix to complete each of these space terms.

5 _____ verse   _____ nova   _____ scope

6 _____ naut   _____ sphere   _____ oid

Write a more formal synonym to replace the word or phrase in **bold**.

7 Be **on your guard**.   _____

8 It was **okay**.   _____

9 The amount was **not enough**.   _____

10 The place was **unfriendly**.   _____

C Sentence work

Shorten the sentence by starting with the verb, rather than a conjunction.

1 Although I was trembling with fear, I turned the key. _____

2 Because she was running fast, she quickly caught up. _____

3 As he gathered his strength, he climbed higher. _____

4 As I was encouraged by the applause, my confidence returned.

_____

5 Underline the adjectives. **Each snowflake is individual and unique.**

6 What do the adjectives tell us about the design of snowflakes? _____

7 Underline the verbs. **As the bulldozers advance, all wildlife flees.**

8 Why has the writer chosen these verbs? _____

9 Why is the comma needed in this sentence? **Has the cat eaten, Jess?**

_____

10 Why is a hyphen needed in this sentence? **I re-sent the emails.**

_____

X There is only one correct answer.   X There is more than one correct answer.

A Warm-up

Change the preposition phrase. Write three different sentences.

The giant stomped over the hill

1 _____

2 _____

3 _____

Change the prefix to make a new word.

4 interrupt → _____

5 transfer → _____

6 interaction → _____

7 telescope → _____

Underline the word that is wrongly spelt.

8 arguable adorable agreable

9 dissbelief disservice dissatisfy

10 referee referal reference

B Word work

Write the correct spelling of the library sign.

1 gimnastiks and phisical edurcation

_____

2 moden forern langwages

_____

3 enginering, desine and tecknolergy

_____

Write two words related to the word in **bold**.

4 **public** _____

5 **memory** _____

6 **origin** _____

Add the correct word.

larva lava

7 volcanic _____

8 caterpillar _____

symbols cymbals

9 I play the _____

10 There were _____ on the map.

C Sentence work

Rewrite the sentence in the passive voice to make it sound impersonal.

1 I sent a letter to the newspaper. _____

2 We will have to cancel the concert. _____

3 We provide a choice of activities. _____

4 I have taken steps to prevent this. _____

Write a question to follow the sentence. Form your questions in different ways.

5 Hanif ran towards the river. _____

6 The path divided. _____

7 I left him to it. _____

Insert a colon and a semi-colon in the correct place in the sentence.

8 We sell a range of snacks rolls, which are homemade cakes and delicious ice creams.

9 Strong gales can cause serious problems roof tiles are dislodged chimneys damaged and branches blown off trees.

10 How else could you present the information? _____

A Warm-up

Continue the sentence using

① **the active voice** The sword _____

_____

② **the passive voice** The sword _____

_____

③ **a relative pronoun** The sword _____

_____

Add a short word to complete the longer word.

④ g ___ t l y
⑤ o ___ i e n t
⑥ a ___ o n e d
⑦ j e ___ e r y

Complete the sentence.

⑧ **Archaeology** is the study of

_____

⑨ **Etymology** is the study of _____

⑩ Underline the **ology** that is **not** a real word.

zoology meteorology snowology sociology

B Word work

Add the missing syllables.

① ex / _____ / _____   *Clue:* put out
② con / _____ / _____   *Clue:* not a vowel

Add the prefix **pre** to complete the words.

③ _____ judice   _____ cede

④ Write the words by their meaning.

_____ go before

_____ a preconceived opinion

Write two words related to the word in **bold**.

⑤ **refer** _____

⑥ **govern** _____

Cross out the incorrect word in the sentence.

⑦ Take my **advice advise**.
⑧ **Practice Practise** every day.
⑨ Let's **device devise** a plan.
⑩ Complete these sentences about the words above.

The verbs end _____

The nouns end _____

C Sentence work

Complete the sentences to show two possible and two certain outcomes.

① If Jack had not climbed the beanstalk _____
② If Cinderella had not lost her shoe _____
③ If Goldilocks had not run away _____
④ If the boy had not cried 'Wolf!' _____

Rewrite the sentence using a more formal style.

⑤ We shouldn't wear jeans to school. _____
⑥ The centre helps old people. _____
⑦ People want the councillors to rethink. _____
⑧ We want money to make up for the mess. _____

⑨ Punctuate the information as **two** sentences, adding the capital letter where necessary.

On average a person in the UK uses 150 litres of water a day in parts of Africa, each person has just ten litres a day.

⑩ Punctuate it again as **one** sentence.

On average a person in the UK uses 150 litres of water a day in parts of Africa, each person has just ten litres a day.

X There is only one correct answer.   X There is more than one correct answer.

A Warm-up

The subject is **umbrellas**. Write a sentence using the given determiner.

1. **all** _____

2. **some** _____

3. **these** _____

Add one letter to make a different word.

4. scare _____

5. through _____

6. lightning _____

Draw a line to join the word to its language of origin.

7. patio   Norwegian

8. ski   Latin

9. chauffeur   Spanish

10. science   French

B Word work

Complete the word sum. Check the spelling carefully.

1. **humour + ous** = _____

2. **disaster + ous** = _____

3. **miracle + ous** = _____

Use a dictionary to write the meaning of the word in **bold**.

4. a **lucid** account _____

5. a **ludicrous** idea _____

6. a **melancholy** song _____

7. a **mediocre** effort _____

Complete the unfinished words in these formal sentences.

8. All empl _____ will be issued with a work per _____ .

9. Please en _____ that you pro _____ a contact number for use in an em _____ .

10. Further details ava _____ on re _____ .

C Sentence work

Rearrange the sentence so that the noun phrase comes at the end.

1. There was a huge bull right in front of me. _____

2. There was the dog, staggering towards him, thin as a rake.

_____

3. The giant beast slowly loomed out of a thin swirling mist.

_____

He won the Olympics and then ~~he won~~ the World Championships.

4. Why has the writer crossed out the words? _____

5. What is this called? Tick one.   ambiguity ____   ellipsis ____   subjunctive ____

Complete the sentence to create a sense of

6. **calm**   Sunlight _____

7. **tension**   Darkness _____

Continue the sentence using a dash, colon or semi-colon, and add another clause.

8. This is a warning _____   9. He waved his fist _____

10. Now he was frightened _____

X There is only one correct answer.   X There is more than one correct answer.

A Warm-up

A tiger has escaped from the local zoo.

Continue the sentence with

1 **an adverb**

2 **a semi-colon**

3 **a conjunction**

Write the correct spelling.

4 receit

5 decietful

6 concieve

Write the day of the week that means

7 **day of the Moon**

8 **day of Saturn**

9 **day of the god Woden**

10 **day of the god Thor**

B Word work

Write the correct spelling.

1 Law and justise in Anglo saxon comunities

2 Roman arcitecture and military strenth

3 Bronze age religon and cullture

Write two words that start with the root.

4 **cert**

5 **spect**

6 **quad**

Write different definitions of each word.

7 **mould** (in arts and crafts)

8 **mould** (in science)

9 **scale** (in science)

10 **scale** (in geography)

C Sentence work

Rewrite the sentence in the passive voice, without mentioning who is responsible.

1 Man's actions force some animals to find new habitats.

2 Man hunted the dodo until it became extinct.

3 People are cutting down large areas of forest.

An apatosaurus was a huge plant-eating dinosaur with an enormously long neck.

4 Why does the writer use this expanded noun phrase?

Write your own expanded noun phrases.

5 The hippopotamus is

6 A stegosaurus was

7 A peacock is

Put a tick if the sentence is correctly punctuated. Put a cross if it is not.

8 If commuters used public transport, the roads would be less crowded.

9 Climate change is a huge concern, experts are worried about Earth's future.

10 Write the incorrect sentence correctly.

X There is only one correct answer. X There is more than one correct answer.

A Warm-up

Write a list of activities as bullet points.

1 **There will be lots of fun activities:**

_____

_____

_____

2 Write a sentence that lists the same information.

_____

_____

_____

Write a word starting with these letters. You can use a dictionary to help you.

3 **h y d** _____

4 **h y g** _____

5 **h y p** _____

6 **h y s** _____

Use word play to write a name for a

7 **hairdresser** _____

8 **fish and chip shop** _____

9 **flower shop** _____

10 **bakery** _____

B Word work

Add single or double consonants to spell the words correctly.

1 **c m**   re ___ o ___ end   a ___ o ___ odate

2 **r s**   emba ___ a ___   ha ___ a ___ ed

3 **c s**   ne ___ e ___ ary   a ___ e ___ ory

Complete the word sum.

4 **global**   + ise   + ation   = _____

5 _____ + _____ + _____ = **civilisation**

6 _____ + _____ + _____ = **Romanisation**

Write a definition of the word in bold.

7 a **brief** visit

brief: _____

8 a design **brief**

brief: _____

9 a **current** news story

current: _____

10 an electric **current**

current: _____

C Sentence work

Complete the subordinate clause using the subjunctive form. Then add a main clause.

1 **If time travel** _____ **possible,** _____

2 **If I** _____ **head teacher,** _____

3 **If the council** _____ **to ban cars in the town centre,** _____

4 What is the purpose of sentences like these? _____

Rewrite the sentence so that it sounds more formal.

5 **Sorry if the building work caused you problems.**

_____

6 **You can't use your camera.** _____

7 **Be sure to have all your papers with you.**

_____

Punctuate and continue the book blurb.

8 **When Lenny the alien joins Class 6 strange things happen –** _____

9 **One stormy night Josh finds shelter in a deserted barn –** _____

10 **Marcie an orphan lives with her gran in Victorian London where she is very happy –** _____

_____

X There is only one correct answer.   X There is more than one correct answer.

A Warm-up

Continue the sentence.

1 If you were to stand in the rain, _____

_____

2 If I were prime minister, _____

_____

3 If it were dark all day, _____

_____

Draw a line to join the dinosaur name to its meaning.

4 megalosaurus   three-horned face

5 triceratops   fast plunderer

6 velociraptor   great lizard

Write the meaning of the word.
You can use a dictionary to help you.

7 **catastrophe** _____

8 **haggard** _____

9 **collaborate** _____

10 **consternation** _____

B Word work

Cross out the words that are wrongly spelt.
Write the correct spellings.

1 The secretry re-signed from the commitee.

_____

2 The professer will re-search it thoroghly.

_____

3 The veicles were queing to reenter.

_____

Add the same suffix to all three words.

ous ity ify

4 sign ____   mod ____   cert ____

5 hazard ____   poison ____   envy ____

6 curious   generous   possible

Write different definitions of each word.

7 **font** (in RE) _____

8 **font** (in IT) _____

9 **colon** (in science) _____

10 **colon** (in literacy) _____

C Sentence work

Rewrite the sentence twice. First make it shorter and more effective. Then make it longer and more effective.

Then they saw that Nina had vanished.

1 **shorter** _____

2 **longer** _____

Complete the more formal version of these sentences using the subjunctive form.

I hope Jade improves her spelling.   **I hope Jason joins the gymnastics club.**

3 It is important that Jade _____

4 I propose that Jason _____

5 Name the punctuation mark used at the end of this sentence.

Peace returned to the planet – for a little while ... _____

6 Why has it been used? _____

Add a comma or a semi-colon.

7 The crowd parted he stood alone.

8 As the fog lifted dawn began to break.

9 Racing past she grabbed the sword.

10 It was frosty I was glad of the hot drink.

X There is only one correct answer.   X There is more than one correct answer.

A Warm-up

Write a sentence using personification.

1. The volcano _____
2. Frost _____
3. The machine _____

aqua auto hyper
mega scope scribe vision

Make up four new words, using these roots and prefixes only. Then write a definition of each word.

4. _____ _____

5. _____ _____

6. _____ _____

7. _____ _____

Write a related word with a different ending.

8. **vegetable** _____
9. **devious** _____
10. **community** _____

B Word work

Use a dictionary to write the correct spelling.

1. kaleidescope _____
2. manoovre _____
3. budgarigar _____
4. parralellogram _____

Write the word to go with the definition.
Use the root in **bold** to help you spell it.

5. _____ (noun)

   the way you **sign** your name

6. _____ (adjective)

   it will **suffice**

7. _____ (adjective)

   out of the **ordinary**

These sentences are about a dance. Underline the words we do **not** use today. Write the words that we would use instead.

8. She doth but very softly go. _____
9. Tis not fast; tis not slow. _____
10. Foot it featly here and there. _____

C Sentence work

We need money to keep the animal shelter open.

Complete the next three sentences to develop this idea.

1. This means _____
2. If _____
3. On the other hand, _____

Rewrite the sentence so the character's actions show their feelings. Use a progressive verb form in the sentence.

4. Mum was angry. _____
5. Bimla was scared. _____
6. Oliver was sad. _____
7. Mr Jacks was happy. _____

Correct the punctuation in the sentence.

8. It seems that banana's are the UKs favourite fruit, we eat more of them than any other fruit.

9. Of course keeping fit, is not just for players of sport fitness is a goal for all.

10. There hidden, below, was the treasure it was just what Jo had always dreamt of.

Now complete Section 3 of the Progress chart on page 46.

X There is only one correct answer.　　X There is more than one correct answer.

43

Proposed road development

There are plans to build a new road in your area. Some local people think this is a good idea and others are against it. A meeting is to be held to discuss the issue. Write a formal notice explaining the plan and inviting people to come to the meeting.

Hints

Before you start:

- think about the form of the writing, the purpose and the audience
- decide what information a notice like this should contain and how it might be organised
- note reasons for the new road, including arguments for and against.

As you write:

- use an appropriate style for a formal notice
- think carefully about the words and grammatical structures you use.

Continue on a separate sheet if necessary.

Check

- When you have finished, check through your writing. Make changes to clarify meaning or enhance the effect.
- Check that everything is grammatically correct.
- Proofread to check spelling and punctuation.

Alone in a crowd

Proofread this extract from a story.

Change anything that does not look or sound correct.

Hints

- Check that everything is clear and sounds right.
- Check that the punctuation has been used correctly and effectively.
- Check that the spelling is correct.

It was incredable one minute I was in the librery thumming throogh a old history book on victorian britain and now well, now where exactly was I. The bookshelves computers and even the building had disapeared, everything had altared, I was in a street that I didnt recragnise.

Nerveously I shrank into the shadows, consious that people were eying me with a mixcher of curiousity and suspition, I have to admit my cloths did look a little out of place, everyone else was dressed like caracters in a seen from 'Oliver Twist' all bussles and magisions hats. Was this someones humourous little joke, there must be a simple explaination.

For the moment I felt abandonned and was desparate to find something or someone familier, in my confussion I set off blindly only narrowly avoiding a collission with a barrow and it's owner.

Watch where yer goin, mate the barrow boy exclaimed. Just arrived from the countery, have you.

Extra

On a separate sheet of paper, continue the dialogue that begins in the final paragraph above. Begin with the narrator's response to the question from the barrow boy.

ENGLISH SKILLS 5 | Progress chart

Name: _____   Class/Set: _____

Teacher's name: _____   Date: _____

Instructions

Read the **'I can' targets** for the section you have just finished.
- Colour the circle **green** if you find it **easy** to do what is described.
- Colour the circle **orange** if you are **getting there**, but still need to work on it.
- Colour the circle **red** if you still find this a **difficult** thing to do.

If there are things that you still find difficult, you can work on them in the next section or in the next book.

Writing sentences

'I can' targets	Section 1	Section 2	Section 3
I can write sentences with more than one clause, varying the position of subordinate clauses.	◯	◯	◯
I can use relative clauses beginning with **who, that, which, where** and **when**.	◯	◯	◯
I can vary sentence length and type to achieve different effects.	◯	◯	◯
I can use modal verbs and adverbs to show degrees of possibility.	◯	◯	◯
I can use expanded noun phrases to give clear, concise information.	◯	◯	◯
I can use the passive voice to change the focus of a sentence.		◯	◯

Using punctuation

	Section 1	Section 2	Section 3
I can punctuate sentences effectively.	◯	◯	◯
I can use commas to separate phrases and clauses, and to clarify meaning.	◯	◯	◯
I can use apostrophes for possession and in contractions.	◯	◯	◯
I can punctuate direct speech and quotations accurately.	◯	◯	◯
I can use brackets, dashes and commas to show a parenthesis.	◯	◯	◯
I can use colons or semi-colons in a list (and punctuate bullet points).		◯	◯
I can use a semi-colon, single dash or colon between main clauses.		◯	◯

Checking grammar

	Section 1	Section 2	Section 3
I can use pronouns effectively, avoiding any ambiguity.	◯	◯	◯
I can use the appropriate tense and the perfect form of verbs.	◯	◯	◯
I can use the grammar and vocabulary features of different text types.	◯	◯	◯
I can use grammar and vocabulary suitable for formal writing.	◯	◯	◯
I can use a range of adverbials to link ideas for cohesion.	◯	◯	◯

Understanding and choosing words

	Section 1	Section 2	Section 3
I can suggest synonyms and antonyms for words.	◯	◯	◯
I can choose words to clarify meaning and for effect.	◯	◯	◯
I can use, understand and choose figurative language, similes and metaphors.	◯	◯	◯
I can suggest formal synonyms for words.	◯	◯	◯
I can explain the different meanings of words in different contexts.	◯	◯	◯
I can use word structure and word origin to work out word meanings.	◯	◯	◯

Spelling

	Section 1	Section 2	Section 3
I can spell words using knowledge of word structure.	◯	◯	◯
I can apply spelling rules for adding a range of prefixes and suffixes.	◯	◯	◯
I can use common letter strings and spelling patterns to spell words.	◯	◯	◯
I can use strategies to help me spell tricky words.	◯	◯	◯
I can choose the correct spelling of homophones.	◯	◯	◯
I can spell words with silent letters.		◯	◯
I can spell words using my knowledge of a word's derivation.			◯

Published by **Schofield & Sims Ltd**, 7 Mariner Court, Wakefield, West Yorkshire WF4 3FL, UK
Telephone 01484 607080
www.schofieldandsims.co.uk

First published in 2011
This edition copyright © Schofield & Sims Ltd, 2017
Second impression 2019

Author: **Carol Matchett**
Carol Matchett has asserted her moral right under the Copyright, Designs and Patents Act, 1988, to be identified as the author of this work.

British Library Cataloguing in Publication Data
A catalogue record for this book is available from the British Library.

Design by **Ledgard Jepson Ltd**
Front cover design by **Peter Grundy**
Printed in the UK by **DG3**

ISBN 978 07217 1412 7

Schofield&Sims

the long-established educational publisher specialising in maths, English and science

English Skills provides regular graded practice to develop pupils' literacy skills throughout Key Stage 2. Fully in line with the statutory requirements of the National Curriculum for English, the series comprises seven pupil books with accompanying answer books, as well as a single teacher's guide. Key areas are constantly revisited, giving the pupils the intensive and rigorous practice that is essential to embed learning and prepare for the Key Stage 2 national tests. The series can also be used as preparation for the 11+ or with older students for catch-up and consolidation.

Each pupil book contains:

- 36 one-page tests, each comprising the following three parts:
  Warm-up: word puzzles, 'warm-up' exercises and revision of earlier learning
  Word work: questions on spelling, word structure and vocabulary
  Sentence work: questions on sentence formation, punctuation and grammar
- three **Writing tasks** and three **Proofreading tasks** to put into practice skills learnt throughout the book
- a **Progress chart** for pupils to record their achievements.

The **English Skills** teacher's guide contains **Entry tests** to help select the appropriate book for each pupil, **Diagnostic checks** to identify and reinforce topics that pupils are finding challenging, and a wide range of photocopiable learning resources. A selection of free downloads is also available.

English Skills 5 covers use of a colon, semi-colon and dash between clauses; sentence variation; question tags; colons and semi-colons in lists; the active and passive voice; ellipsis; editing sentences for effect; and vocabulary and grammar for formal writing. The accompanying answer book, **English Skills 5 Answers**, contains answers to all the questions in **English Skills 5**.

English Skills		English Skills	
Introductory Book	978 07217 1402 8	**Introductory Book Answers**	978 07217 1403 5
English Skills 1	978 07217 1404 2	**English Skills 1 Answers**	978 07217 1405 9
English Skills 2	978 07217 1406 6	**English Skills 2 Answers**	978 07217 1407 3
English Skills 3	978 07217 1408 0	**English Skills 3 Answers**	978 07217 1409 7
English Skills 4	978 07217 1410 3	**English Skills 4 Answers**	978 07217 1411 0
English Skills 5	978 07217 1412 7	**English Skills 5 Answers**	978 07217 1413 4
English Skills 6	978 07217 1414 1	**English Skills 6 Answers**	978 07217 1415 8
English Skills Teacher's Guide	978 07217 1416 5		

ISBN 978-07217-1412-7

9 780721 714127

ISBN 978 07217 1412 7
Key Stage 2
Age range 7–11+ years
£3.95 (Retail price)

For further information and to place your order visit
www.schofieldandsims.co.uk or telephone 01484 607080

WELCOME TO THIS BOOK

The **English Skills** tests give you plenty of practice in using your literacy skills. With regular practice, your skills will quickly improve. Each **English Skills** book is divided into three sections. When you finish a section, complete one column of the **Progress chart** on page 46. Full instructions are given. The **Glossary** below may help you to tackle the tests. It gives examples that may help you to understand a question.

GLOSSARY

active voice	where the subject of the sentence performs the action (e.g. **The dog chased the cat.** The dog is the subject of the sentence and performs the action.)
ambiguity	when the meaning is not clear. Ambiguity can be caused by overuse of pronouns or by missing punctuation (e.g. **Slow hedgehogs crossing**).
bullet points	a way of presenting a number of points as a clear list
cohesion	when all parts of a text clearly fit together. Achieved through the use of linking adverbials (e.g. **consequently**), pronouns and repeated words.
colon	looks like this **:** and is used to introduce a list or to link two main clauses where the second clause expands on the first
condition	where one thing depends on something else (e.g. We could build a snowman **if it snows**.)
dash	looks like this **–** and is used to add an extra piece of information on to the end of a sentence. Two dashes can be used as an alternative to brackets/commas to show a parenthesis in a sentence.
ellipsis	omitting words to avoid repetition (e.g. He saw me and **he** ran). Also refers to the punctuation mark that looks like this **...** and shows that something is incomplete.
formal language	the language and sentence structures used in 'formal' situations
hyphen	looks like this **-** and is used to join two words or parts of words together (e.g. **mix-up, non-smoking, re-enter**). It can help avoid ambiguity (e.g. I will **re-cover** the settee).
informal language	the everyday language and sentence structures that we use when communicating with people we know. It is more often used in spoken language.
mnemonic	a literary device that helps you remember something
modal verb	verbs such as **might, could** and **will** that are used with other verbs (e.g. to show possibility – it **might** rain)
object	someone or something that receives the action in a sentence (e.g. The dog chased the **cat**.)
parenthesis	an extra piece of information added into the middle of a sentence (e.g. Daniel James, **aged 10**, was the winner.)
passive voice	where the subject of the sentence receives the action (e.g. **The cat was chased by the dog.** In this sentence the cat, the subject of the sentence, is receiving the action.)
personification	a type of metaphor where a non-human subject is described in human terms
pun	a humorous play on words, using words that sound the same but have different meanings
question tag	a phrase added to the end of a statement to make it into a question (e.g. You will come, **won't you?**)
semi-colon	looks like this **;** and is used to separate items in a list of phrases, or between two closely linked main clauses
subject	the person or thing the sentence is about; it is usually the performer of the action (e.g. The **dog** buried the bone.)
subjunctive	a special form of verb used in formal speech and writing to refer to imaginary situations (e.g. if I **were** the queen ...)

English Skills 5

- Noun
- Adjective
- Verb

Name